TEXTING HARRY

By Connie Podesta

www.textingharrybook.com   www.conniepodesta.com

It was my lucky day.

Bumped to first class—empty seat to my left.

Light snow falling. Headed home.

After three back-to-back-to-back speaking engagements, I was exhausted. But now, four hours of total peace and quiet. I could finally relax and catch up on my life.

Then ... he walked in.

AN OLDER MAN WITH A
RUMPLED SUIT
AND LOOSE HANGING TIE
PUSHED
HIS WAY ONTO THE PLANE.

OH, NO.
COULD THIS BE
THE END
OF MY LONG AWAITED
SOLITUDE?

I froze as he said

4A?

Cue The Phantom of the Opera soundtrack.

Cue fingernails running down a chalkboard.

I stood as he pushed a grin through his grit and squeezed passed me.

I'm Harry.

Just perfect, I thought as I managed a tiny smile.

Great.

My husband had made special arrangements
to meet me at the airport. I had to let him know
I wouldn't be home on time.

FLIGHT
60

DELAYED
MIN.

Texting? asked my somewhat nosy seatmate.

Yep. I did not want this conversation.

Hmm.

Seems all I see anymore in the airport are people thumbing their phones with their heads down. I don't get it.

I couldn't help myself. I had to respond ... I guess.

That's true, I replied.

But have you ever tried it?

Nah.

I don't get into all the techno-trend stuff. I'm kind of old-school I guess. But it works for me.

If it's possible to swagger while talking, Harry was.

Besides, I've got enough going on. I don't need to worry about tripping over my own feet t-e-x-t-i-n-g.

I was about to respond when ...

DING!

Thank goodness!

Saved by the proverbial text-ding. As I checked my phone I could see Harry out of the corner of my eye leaning in for a peek.

TXT:

—OK. BAD WEATHER?

As I thumbed a response, I thought how to respond to Harry. I was tired and didn't want to sound curt.

Maybe I could help him understand.

Maybe I could understand him.

Yeah, I said,

I can remember, at first, thinking like that about texting. But the more I did it, the more it began to make sense. Sometimes it's the perfect way to talk to somebody.

I don't know, piped Harry.

To me it's not talking at all.

Pretty soon we'll all be communicating digitally to each other instead of speaking. The other day at work the guy in the cubicle next to me emailed me about going to lunch with him.

He was getting worked up.

For crying out loud!

I was right there. Just stand up and ask me. I don't need a screen to communicate.

I like the old-fashioned face-to-face stuff. I don't need fifty different ways to talk to someone.

Harry clearly wanted his point of view heard. And I had to admit, it had some merits. So I swallowed my dream of a cozy flight filled with reading and napping and decided to engage. I am always up for a good debate.

No, you're right, I admitted.

Sometimes it does get a bit overwhelming.

Harry hung his head and rubbed his eyes. The man was visibly exhausted. I could see that just talking about change was stressful to him.

He squeezed the back of his neck and continued, **Just when I think I have one thing down, I have to learn something else.**

Will it ever stop?

DING!

I froze.

I felt like I was committing the worst of transgressions. I could see Harry shaking his head in frustration as I read my husband's response.

TXT:

2 BAD ABOUT THE WEATHER. <3. TTYL.

I smiled.

OK, look at this.

I decided to show Harry instead of trying to explain texting to him.

I know you're skeptical, but just humor me.

I was as diplomatic as I could be. This was going to take some doing on my part.

See that symbol? I asked.

That's my husband telling me he loves me. In a few short lines I was able to tell him about our delay and that I miss him and he was able to answer me back in seconds.

And what does TTYL mean?

Oh, that means I'll talk to you later.

Harry looked surprised.

Hmm. Looks like a different language to me.

Well, in a way it is. It's like a language shortcut—similar to your computer ...

Yeah, I see that. But why not just call him and tell him?

Well, in this situation a whole conversation isn't necessary. He just needed a quick note from me telling him what was up.

Harry was nodding. I could tell that I piqued his interest. So I kept going.

Don't you hate it when you have no choice but to listen to someone else's private conversation and there's no escape?

Absolutely.
That's annoying.

I agree.

Well, texting my husband allows me AND YOU some privacy.

I can tell him we're delayed and that I love him without anyone eavesdropping on my conversation.

OK,

I'll give you that texting is more private.

Fine. But for me, it's also all the "newness" about it.

New equipment to learn, new language to figure out, new everything it seems.

Plus, it follows you everywhere. No more quiet vacations or weekend getaways.

Emails and texts and whatever else

... there's no escaping.

Harry was determined, it seemed, to remain closed to the wonderful rewards learning something new can bring.

One more try, I thought.

I'll give him one more try. After that, the past is all his if he wants to stay there.

Right, I responded,

but what about all the good things about texting? Like keeping in touch with people you care about even if you are short on time. Or re-connecting with old friends or keeping tabs on your teenagers. Now that is huge!

We both chuckled at that.

Harry shot a wry smile.
I was beginning to break through.

FOLKS,
THIS IS YOUR CAPTAIN AGAIN.
**I'M SORRY TO REPORT
THAT WE HAVE TO
DELAY TAKE-OFF
ANOTHER HOUR
DUE TO THE ICY
CONDITIONS.**

Now that is information we didn't want in
any form—talking or texting,
I quipped.

Both of us laughed.
The mood continued to lighten.

**It's like I woke up one day and the
world went out and got in a big hurry,
for no apparent reason.**
Harry took off his tie and unbuttoned his top button.

I can understand that. You almost can't
blink in today's world without falling
behind in some way.

Call it a sixth sense but I somehow knew that
Harry wanted to communicate more than he
let on.

By the way Harry, sorry if I was distant
earlier. I was tired and forgot my manners.

I'm Connie.

Oh, no worries.

I figured you'd had a long day too.

That's for sure.

Are you from this area? I asked.

Used to be.

I got transferred awhile back—every five years it seems. I was just in visiting an old client.

You?

Well, like you, I've moved around a lot. I live in Dallas now, but I used to live in Connecticut so it's been awhile since I've seen snow. I forget how beautiful it is.

No thank you.

I can deal without the winter driving. Not to mention the wind and ice.

I interrupted before he could start griping again.

Do you have any kids?

I do.
He grinned.

Two grown daughters.

So do I. Any grandkids?

Yes.
Now he started to beam.

I have one grandson named Chad.

Oh, I bet you love that!

When Chad was a
little guy, I was
his best buddy.

But a few years ago they moved away. Now we only connect a couple of times a year. You know, holidays, if we're lucky.

I can relate, Harry.

My oldest daughter lives in another state so it makes it really tough to keep in touch with my granddaughters.

He nodded.

Plus Chad is fourteen now and is so busy. I don't remember being that busy when I was fourteen. I hardly ever get to talk to him.

Well, I prodded,

how do you stay in contact with him?

I don't.

Well, I mean, my wife talks to my daughter all the time. But when I get a chance to talk with Chad it's kind of awkward.

Like neither one of us knows what to say.

Harry shrugged as though it didn't matter, but I could tell he cared.

He wanted to be closer to Chad.

TIME TO TURN ON MY INNER THERAPIST, I THOUGHT.

What does he like to do?

Any hobbies? Sports?

Oh yeah, he's a great athlete. He's on the school soccer team. They had a big playoff game last week. That's the kind of thing I really miss seeing. But I can't be everywhere at once. I need a super-power, or something.

That's when it hit me.

I had to make a quick decision. Do I bring it up again and risk blowing our nice little conversation? Or just let it slide, finish the conversation, show some empathy, and put the headphones on?

I went for it.

Well, I'm not a superhero, but I do have a super-powerful idea that might help you get Chad's attention.

Huh?

I caught him off guard.

Would you like to learn a little trick that will allow you to be everywhere at once?

I would say yes, but there's no way. He's got too much going on and even when I do get him on the phone—we have a hard time relating to each other. I don't think kids even know how to communicate these days.

They do—just in a different way than you're used to. You either have to do something to get in the game or you'll be watching from the sidelines.

In order to keep up with my granddaughters, I had to learn to "talk" their way.

What do you mean "their way"? Is talking on the phone so hard?

No, but it's not what they know. They are the reason I started texting to begin with.

**Ha!
I knew it. More techno-babble. That was pretty sly, Connie.**

Was that a grin on Harry's face?

Very funny. Harry, my granddaughters don't realize it, but their generation has progressed light years ahead of mine— uh, and yours. Just like the telephone progressed into the cell phone, right? We either move with it or we are left behind. Literally.

Sure, I get that.

You're right. Maybe I should just stop complaining about it.

But ...

No "buts," Harry.

I asked Harry for his phone. He complied, but not without a groan. Turns out Harry's phone rocked. It was already set up to receive texts and emails. He just needed someone to help him figure it all out.

OK, if it's alright with you, I'd like to show you how easy this really is. It's just another form of talking.

You'll be a pro in no time.

Harry still looked a little hesitant, but I could tell he was also a little excited.

Discovery has a way of igniting our imagination. Harry was about to be lit up with new possibilities.

Fine.

I'll try it once.

But he's in school now.

No problem.

He'll get it after class. You're stalling. C'mon Harry. I grinned my challenge and he responded.

OK, fine. I'll see if his info is in my address book.

Address book? Are you serious? I laughed.

Yeah, I couldn't figure out the whole "contact" thing so I stayed old school.

You and your "old school." Ha! We both laughed while Harry found the info along with a picture of Chad.

This picture of him is a few years old. His braces are off now.

Harry, Chad will be so embarrassed if he finds out you're walking around with that old photo. He grinned.

I let Harry play around with my phone and look at my vacation photos while I programmed Chad's info into his phone.

OK Harry. You're all set. Moment of truth.

Harry looked down at his phone apprehensively.

What am I going to say?

Maybe try telling him that you're proud he won his game.

He began typing as I explained each step.

Harry stumbled over his thumbs. The text was a mess, but I urged him to keep at it.

Don't worry, I said, you'll get it. It took me forever to get the hang of it. But it'll be worth it. Trust me.

Ugh!

I'm too old for this, he said in frustration, still fumbling with his phone.

Nonsense. My mother is eighty and texts me all the time.

Really?

Yeah, Harry, it's not about your age. It's about refusing to learn new things. The moment you fold and say "I'm not going to learn something new," you're done. Our bodies may get older but that doesn't mean we have to age mentally as well.

No, no. You're right. I think sometimes it's more about feeling exhausted trying to keep up with it all.

But isn't resisting change even more exhausting? I believe that learning new things and keeping in touch with the world around us keeps us young.

BOOM.

SOMETHING CLICKED IN HARRY.

HE RESONATED WITH WHAT I WAS SAYING.

ALL OF A SUDDEN **HE SEEMED REVITALIZED.**

I'm ready. Let's text.

OK Harry. Give it a go.

CHAD, THIS IS GRAMPS. HEARD YOU WON YOUR SOCCER GAME. GOOD JOB.

Nice.

Now hit the green button to send it.

Please God, let Chad respond, I thought.

Nothing ...

Awkward pause in conversation ...

Both of us sat there just staring at his phone.

How am I supposed to know when he ...

DING!

Whoa. What was that? What just ...

It's probably Chad. After all, Harry, there
aren't a lot of people in your contact list
yet, I said with a chuckle.

TXT:

LOL.
GRAMPS! DUDE!
DIDN'T KNOW YOU
COULD TEXT. COOL.
HERE'S A PIC OF ME
AT THE GAME.

What does "LOL" mean? And did he really just call me "dude"?

It means "laughing out loud." Basically, he's happy you texted him. Plus, he sent you a picture. Harry, it worked. You did it!

The next few moments were a mixture of pride and excitement. Harry and Chad had finally connected.

TXT:

WHAT WAS THE SCORE?

DING! **TXT:**

1-0 VICTORY OVER #3 PANTHERS!

DING! **TXT:**

I SCORED THE LONE GOAL OF THE GAME IN THE 38TH MINUTE.

Harry was ecstatic. Not only did he learn something new and invigorating, but the rain cloud he seemed to always carry around with him had vanished. He shifted his thinking and his attitude followed. It was amazing to watch..

Imagine how many people you could stay in touch with if you just texted people every once in awhile.

Hmm ...

maybe I should try texting my daughter. That would be a game changer.

Oh yeah? Why is that?

Well, we have a hard time communicating sometimes. We always seem to find a way to argue. We are both stubborn and are overly sensitive to the other's tone of voice.

I think texting her would be a great idea.

Try it.

Harry was catching on. And fast.

TXT:

DEBBIE, THIS IS DAD. HOPE EVERYTHING IS GOING WELL.

Should I say anything else? I'm not really a "love, dad" kind of guy.

How about "pcm"? It means "please call me."

Perfect. He hit the send button.

DING!

TXT:

DAD! DIDN'T KNOW U COULD TEXT! COOL. OFF WORK TOMORROW. CALL YOU IN THE MORNING. LOVE U.

Harry had changed into a new person. He walked on the plane exhausted and stressed out but was now happy and excited. He was learning to act on new ideas rather than react to them. He didn't just have a new perspective on change; he had new perspective on life.

THE OLD HARRY WAS BACK.

Wow.

I feel like I just had a major breakthrough.

Harry you did. This is great.

I feel like I just got done with a techno-therapy session! You should go into business.

Funny ... this is actually what I do for a living, I replied with a laugh.

Oh wow. Really?

Yeah, you know ... I guess you could say I'm a change instigator!

Can't say I'm surprised. You helped me break out of my funk. My wife would die if she knew I was actually taking advice from a life-coach-change-person.

She might be surprised, but would be glad someone helped you move into the present day!

We laughed.

Well Connie, thanks for talking about all this. It's hard to believe I let myself get so bogged down.

Turns out, change isn't so bad.

That's because you made a conscious decision to move past your initial negative reaction and chose a positive action instead.

By now Harry and I were pretty comfortable with one another. His guard was down and I was in familiar territory.

I run into people every day who say they hate to let go of the past. And I tell them that letting go of the past is what brings us into the future.

It is important to view change as a step forward—not a step backward.

Our first reaction

to change

determines

how we handle

and accept it

from that moment on.

But ... well, I don't need to get on my soapbox with you.

Sorry.

No, no. It's good, you're right. It all boiled down to a choice I was too lazy to make:

learn to communicate differently or be left behind.

It was like all my negative thoughts were piling up on each other. They were weighing me down, sucking away my energy to do anything positive.

You know Harry, maybe you should hop on the speaking circuit with me. You're quite good at this.

Well, I'm not there yet. But the more we talk about this stuff, the more I'm thinking I should use this approach in my job. With my boss.

I'm sure it would translate.

Communication problems?

Well, you could say that.

He's twenty years younger than me. And I hate to admit it—but it drives me crazy. Part of me thinks I could be his dad, the other part wants to kick his... well, you get the picture.

That's a tough position to be in for sure.

I have twice the amount of experience he does!

Right, but is he qualified for the job?

Yes, he's qualified.

I just hate taking orders from a kid.

What if you looked at the situation and realized that leadership is a two-way street. You have a lot of experience that could really help him.

You know ... take this new approach we've been discussing.

Hmm. But he's my boss. How does that work?

Look at it like this. Just because he's your boss doesn't mean you can't still be a good leader.

Huh?

YOU CAN INFLUENCE HIS
LEADERSHIP
BY BEING A STRONG LEADER YOURSELF.

TAKE MORE INITIATIVE TO
KEEP IN CONTACT WHILE
OUT IN THE FIELD.

OFFER INSIGHT
HE MIGHT NOT BE AWARE OF.
THAT KIND OF STUFF. YOU
COULD TREAT THE RELATIONSHIP
ALMOST LIKE YOU ARE
COLLABORATORS.

JUST CHANGE YOUR
PERSPECTIVE
... LIKE YOU DID WITH
TEXTING.

I suppose I could implement my new communication method.

He picks up his phone and shakes it with a smile.

Great idea!

Do it. Shoot him a text and let him know how your meeting went.

In a flurry Harry rattled off a quick text to his boss and closed his phone. It was like he transformed right in front of me.

Wait till he gets that text.

I just closed a deal with a big client today. He'll go nuts.

DING!

Man, I love how fast this is! he said as he flipped his phone open.

TXT:

BAU. CONGRATS.
TOUGH CUSTOMER. U DID
GOOD! DIDN'T KNOW U
COULD TEXT.

BAU?
Does that mean business as usual?

Sure does. You're catching on. But it really should be BAUO—business as usual is over. We are going to have to move way beyond expectations if we want to stay in the game in today's competitive environment. What "used to be" isn't good enough anymore.

Harry and I looked at each other, made a toast with our coffee mugs, and got ready for takeoff.

By the time we got in the air Harry and I were starving. We put our work away when they began serving dinner. After the long delay even the airplane food tasted good.

Harry and I enjoyed a wonderful conversation about his work and what he could do to improve his perspective on change, his communication skills-you name it, we covered it. It was like our own little brainstorming session.

By the end of our time, not only was Harry excited about texting, he was asking questions about the latest in social media. He was taking the initiative when it came to change. This was his new beginning.

Hey, now that we're old friends I was wondering if I could ask something. It's kind of personal. But everything we've talked about has been personal.

I laughed in agreement.

Sure.

What's up?

Well, it's Jean ... my wife.

Things between us haven't been great lately.

Are you asking me how to fix your wife?

I waited with a knowing glance.

No. I get it. I can't fix her—but I can change myself. Right? The truth is, I've been pretty hard to handle at home recently—the stress and everything really put me in a nasty mood.

I find that hard to believe.

Harry laughed, threw his hands up in surrender and said **Touché.**

Ha. Believe me, I realize I need to do a clean sweep with all of my relationships. With Jean, I think it's that she just picks up on my bad attitude. She thinks I'm a grump. In fact, she calls me Grumpy Harry.

Has she asked you what's bothering you?

Yeah. But I always tell her it's nothing. It makes her so mad.

Harry, here's the deal with women.

We can sense immediately when something is wrong with the people we love. By keeping your wife at bay and refusing to open up, you are making her feel left out. She wants to be there for you. And that's a really good thing.

Harry, I know sometimes you might get bogged down with stress and work schedules. But think of the ally you could have with Jean. Don't you think that having her as a true partner instead of just another person you try to pacify would make life easier for you?

That's a good point.

I really want things back how they used to be.

We used to be best friends.

LADIES AND GENTLEMEN, THANKS FOR YOUR PATIENCE THIS EVENING. PLEASE FIND YOUR SEATS AND KEEP YOUR SEATBELTS FASTENED AS WE MAKE OUR FINAL DESCENT INTO DALLAS/FORT WORTH.

Wow, that didn't take long. Harry was snappy with his new positive outlook on life.

See how time flies when you're starting a new chapter in life? Harry nodded and smiled.

Back to our discussion about Jean. I didn't have time to ... I didn't take the time to call her before we left. I didn't want to get in a fight because she'll be picking me up.

I know all I did was delay the inevitable.

You didn't let her know about our delay?

Harry!

Harry didn't need much prodding after that.

The moment we touched down he flipped open his phone, passed me a hopeful glance, and tapped out a text to Jean.

I'm done avoiding confrontation.

Nice, Harry.

Take it from a woman. She will love that you texted her. If you guys don't talk we take that to mean, "He doesn't care about me."

He took some extra time with this text. He wanted to get it right.

Um ... a little help?

I'm stuck.

What else should I say?

Well, maybe offer her a date night for being late. And maybe something tender or romantic to end it.

Uh, I'm not the romantic ...

Ah! No more making excuses, Harry. I can and will be romantic.

Yes, good for you, I exclaimed. You don't have to get all mushy. Just be honest.

Time to finish up, Harry. We're almost to the gate.

Ah! How should I end it?

Did you tell her you love her?

Uh ...

Harry!

OK. OK.

Can you handle "ALML"? It means "all my love." Then put a bunch of X's at the end. Kind of like sending notes in high school.

Harry blushed and grinned.

Mmm. High school with Jean.

Great memories!

Harry held up his phone for a final approval.

TXT:

SORRY I'M LATE.
MISSED U.
THX 4 PICKING ME UP.
GLAD TO BE HOME.
HOW ABOUT I TAKE U
2 DINNER? UR CHOICE.
ALML. XXXX.

Perfect, Harry. Now hit send.

It's done.

Just in time!

the pilot spoke over the loudspeakers,

LADIES AND GENTLEMEN, WE HAVE FINALLY REACHED OUR GATE,

LET ME AGAIN APOLOGIZE FOR THE DELAY. THANK YOU FOR CHOOSING TO FLY WITH US.

A smattering of applause and cheers rang through the cabin.

As Harry and I walked down the jetway together we heard a familiar sound.

DING!

Jean? I asked.

Harry held up his phone with an apprehensive smile, and then read the text.

C'mon Harry!

I'm dying to know. What did she say?

Not sure if it was the Texas air or not but Harry's eyes looked a bit misty.

He read the text out loud:

TXT:

HARRY,

SWEETEST NOTE.

LOVE YOU 2.

PS WHEN DID U

THAT WAS THE

MISSED AND

DINNER SOUNDS GR8.

LEARN 2 TEXT?

You owe me big time, I said with a mischievous grin.

Harry's face brightened as we walked toward the exit.

Harry, I said as we stopped to part ways,

I really enjoyed talking to you. You're a very special person.

Thanks for the memory!

No. The pleasure was all mine, he said shaking my hand warmly.

Thanks for helping me find the guy I used to be. And to think we almost didn't meet.

What do you mean?

I never fly first class. I got upgraded at the last minute.

4A wasn't supposed to be my seat!

Oh yes it was, I thought. I didn't tell him I also had a last minute upgrade. We were supposed to meet. That much was clear to me.

We walked into the warm Dallas evening and gave each other one final wave, then headed to our spouses in the parking lot.

I was greeted by a big hug and kiss from my husband.

I missed you.

Ah, music to a woman's ears. And, as he shut the door I looked out the back window to see Harry and Jean caught in a warm embrace—the kind that says, "I love you" without words.

Tired?

**Not really. In fact, I feel great!
How about you?**

I'm great, too, especially now that you're home.

DING!

I reached down and retrieved my phone from my purse.

Ha! I laughed as I read:

TXT:

THX TO U GRUMPY HARRY IS NOW TEXTING HARRY.

PS MY WIFE SAYS THX 2.

Something funny? asked my husband.

I thought about Harry and what a difference a
few hours had made in his perspective on life.
It was amazing how much impact a little bit of
change could make. I reached for my husband's
hand and nodded,

yes, something funny.

Something wonderful.

Something unforgettable.

Something life-changing.

NOTE FROM CONNIE

I hope you enjoyed taking a ride with Harry and me. It was certainly a plane ride I will never forget. Isn't it amazing how a simple shift in attitude can make all the difference in the world? So many of my clients and audience members tell me they are in the same frame of mind as Harry: confused, overwhelmed, frustrated and exhausted with a constant barrage of new ideas. So get on board with me while I give you a few tips that can help you twofold:

1. cope with change;

2. help someone else who is trying to deal with change.

Good luck and Bon Voyage!

WANT TO INSPIRE CHANGE?

CAN'T HELP BEFORE YOU HEAR

Hear—don't just listen—to what people are saying to you. It's often difficult for people to communicate how they feel about change. What they say at first might not be their real concern. Listening without judging will help them open up. You can't help them through change until you know what it is about the change that is holding them back.

EMPOWER, DON'T EMBITTER

Most people don't like being told what to do, especially if it means changing their habits, actions, or routines. On the other hand, most people do like to be involved in something new and exciting if they have the opportunity to participate and share ideas. There has to be some ownership on their part so they can support the change and justify their part in making it happen.

SOLUTIONS LEAD TO NEW BEHAVIORS

Change requires people to develop new patterns and behaviors. In order for people to be willing to do that, they must see a need in their life. Help them make that connection. Show them how this change will have a positive impact on their personal or professional situation. To successfully embrace change, they must believe that the results of this change will help them do better, be better, or live better.

WANT TO CHANGE?

GET RID OF YOUR EGO

Be as honest with yourself as possible. Being aware of what you avoid and resist are clues into your nature and personality. Change requires that we put our ego aside and look at the bigger picture. We are never the only ones who are affected by our choice to change or not to change. Viewing change as a means to improving skills, developing healthier relationships, or becoming a better person is a strong incentive to letting go of some old patterns.

LEARN NEW STUFF ON YOUR OWN

Be accountable for your own actions and choices. It is impossible to change for the better when you blame outside factors (the economy, your parents, your boss, your "luck") for your situation in life. Change will be successful only if you have made a conscious choice for it to be.

Sabotaging change is not taking charge of your life—it's just avoiding what life has put in front of you.

LEARN, THEN APPLY

Learn to ACT, rather than REACT. Taking positive action means you have listened, weighed the pros and cons, done your homework, and looked at the total picture. REACTION means you did none of the above, and instead reacted (usually selfishly) to a situation. Change is not easy for most people—so first reactions are not to be trusted, by you or anyone else. Take a step back and give change a chance before you decide it's not going to work.

MORE ABOUT CONNIE PODESTA

- Book Connie for your next event. Her topics include change, leadership, sales, relationships and communication. A guaranteed success!

- Imagine having Connie as your personal executive coach so you can move your life and career to a whole new level!

- Learn more about Connie's other books, DVD's and training materials. Tons of information you can use and share with others!

CONTACT CONNIE TODAY!

www.conniepodesta.com

972-596-5501

Texting Harry is a great gift book for employees, customers, family and friends.

If you would like to order additional copies of this book or to inquire about customized versions of this book, please visit us at **www.textingharrybook.com** or call us at **(866) 749-9419.**

Our books are not sold in stores — only direct from SML Books, our authors, and select distributors.